GraphicDesign&

GraphicDesign&
publishing intelligent, vivid books that explore how graphic design connects with all other things and the value it brings.

www.graphicdesignand.com

GW00567973

Page 1:
Great Expectations

Seventy graphic solutions

Page 1: Great Expectations

An unusual typographic experiment, this GraphicDesign& Literature title explores the relationship between design and the reading of a page.

Showing the responses of 70 international graphic designers when posed with the same brief – to lay out the first page of Charles Dickens's novel *Great Expectations* – and including rationales from each contributor, this is a perfect companion piece to **Golden Meaning**.

Contributors include:
A Practice for Everyday Life
Cartlidge Levene
Experimental Jetset
John Morgan studio
KarlssonWilker
Ellen Lupton
Luke Hayman / Pentagram
Morag Myerscough
Erik Spiekermann
Oded Ezer

£15 + p&p

**Winner
50 Best Books 2012
Design Observer**

**A wonderful idea
It's Nice That**

**A fascinating range of responses
Huffington Post**

**Thoughtful and surprising
Wallpaper***

lecturis

printer / publisher /// for creative industries /// www.lecturis.com

Atlas of the conflict

designer
Joost Grootens
publisher
010
Winner Leipzig 2011,
goldene letter
Best Book Design
of the World

**Irma Boom:
The Architecture
of the Book**

designer
Irma Boom
publisher
Lecturis
XXL edition also
available

**Catherine de Smet
Pour une critique du
design graphique**

designer
deValence
publisher
B42

Nono Reinhold

designer
Wim Crouwel
publisher
Lecturis

**Sources in the Air,
David Maljkovic**

designer
Mevis & Van Deursen
publisher
JRP / Ringier

**Stedelijk
Architecture**

designer
Mevis & Van Deursen
publisher
**Stedelijk Museum /
Nai010**

Golden Meaning
Fifty-five graphic experiments

GraphicDesign& is a pioneering publishing house dedicated to creating intelligent, vivid books that explore how graphic design connects with all other things and the value that it brings. Established by Lucienne Roberts and Rebecca Wright, GraphicDesign& partners graphic designers with experts from other fields to inform, educate, entertain and provoke – and to challenge perceptions about what and who graphic design is for.

www.graphicdesignand.com

Golden Meaning
a **GraphicDesign& Mathematics** title
[WFG& AM/AX]

GraphicDesign&

Golden Meaning
Fifty-five graphic experiments

1:

1.618...

Editors
Lucienne Roberts
Rebecca Wright
with
Alex Bellos

A **GraphicDesign&** book

First published in 2014 by
GraphicDesign&
31 Great Sutton Street
London EC1V 0NA
UK

+44 [0]20 7490 8880
info@graphicdesignand.com
www.graphicdesignand.com

978 0 9572381 1 4

———————

Designed by
LucienneRoberts+

Printed and bound by
Lecturis BV

Distributed by
GraphicDesign&

The moral rights of the contributors
have been asserted.

© GraphicDesign& 2014

———————

GraphicDesign& is happy
to be working in association
with printers Lecturis for
this publication.

10 9 8 7 6 5 4 3 2 1

A CIP catalogue record for this book
is available from the British Library.

While every effort has been made
to ensure all factual information
contained in this book is correct, in
some cases the data and calculations
are open to interpretation. All
reasonable attempts have been
made to trace the copyright holders
of images reproduced in this book.
If any attribution has been omitted,
the publisher will endeavour to
amend in any subsequent editions.

Contents

Golden Meanings
alphabetical contributor list

Preface
Lucienne Roberts
Rebecca Wright

On GraphicDesign&

We first discussed the premise that underpins GraphicDesign& in Amsterdam, during a research trip for our book *Design Diaries: Creative Process in Graphic Design*. We had taken refuge from winter rain in the café of the Stedelijk Museum CS. We talked about the projects included in our book and enthused about how they demonstrated what graphic design does best – connect with the rest of the world – and bemoaned the fact that the essentially outward-looking nature of our profession is seldom made explicit. Gradually an idea took shape. GraphicDesign&. The clue is in the name of course...

GraphicDesign& publishes books exploring the symbiotic nature of graphic design practice. Graphic design is always inextricably partnered with something else and each GraphicDesign& project connects graphic design to one of a myriad of subject areas. *Golden Meaning* is a GraphicDesign& Mathematics title.

On Golden Meaning

GraphicDesign& is concerned with how graphic design connects with the wider world. One of our objectives is to reach a non-design audience. With this in mind, we thought it would make sense for our first two titles to pair graphic design with the 'core subjects' English and Maths. We published *Page 1: Great Expectations*, a GraphicDesign& Literature title, in 2012, showing the responses of 70 graphic designers to the same brief: to lay out the first page of Charles Dickens's novel *Great Expectations*. This comparative exercise proved popular and demonstrated the expectations, differences and nuances signalled via typography and design.

Golden Meaning is a companion piece to *Page 1*, comprising the responses of 55 graphic designers and image-makers whose brief was to communicate one of the most famous and controversial concepts in mathematics, the golden mean. Often cited as the secret of true beauty, it might seem an obvious choice for the focus of our book – but the idea didn't come easily.

We were lucky to have mathematician, *Guardian* blogger and author of bestseller *Alex's Adventures in Numberland* and of *Alex through the Looking-Glass* Alex Bellos as adviser. One of Alex's goals is to make his subject more accessible and inclusive. Made curious by our premise that designers and image-makers might be best placed to help in doing just that, he met us for coffee. We discussed possible ideas for the book's focus. Alex patiently scribbled diagrams on napkins, suggested references that might inspire and gradually introduced us to his world, while we scratched our heads.

In the meantime, and at Alex's suggestion, we bought a facsimile of Oliver Byrne's *The Elements of Euclid* (originally published in 1847) and re-read Chapter 8 of Alex's book, appropriately called Gold Finger. In a quiet moment we also re-read some of *Page 1*... All points suddenly converged on the golden mean. Like many illustrious practitioners before him (think typographer Jan Tschichold's 'golden canon of page construction') Erik Spiekermann explained how he used the book's format, a golden rectangle, to determine his *Page 1* layout. Our maths book would also be a golden rectangle so the answer was staring us in the face!

On the brief

Although a simple notion, the golden mean is hard to explain. As with all GraphicDesign& projects, our ambition was to show how the knowledge and practice of graphic designers, typographers and image-makers is uniquely capable of shedding light on ideas. Working alongside Alex, we drafted a brief that was relatively open in asking contributors to communicate, demonstrate or explore the golden mean. As further reading, we sent Alex's chapter on the golden mean alongside the brief and, to ensure that Alex's comments on the results would be impartial, his colleague James Grime liaised directly with any contributors who had tricky mathematics-related questions. An important part of the brief was asking designers to write a rationale explaining their design decisions. These rationales are often significant adjuncts to the design. We didn't deliberate for too long on how many contributors to include – 55 is a number in the Fibonacci series, the number sequence closely connected to the golden mean.

Introduction
Alex Bellos

───────

The golden mean is a number: 1.618*
But it is not just a number...

*In fact, the number only
begins 1.618. It actually
continues forever,
with its decimal digits
following no repeating
pattern. We use the
shortened version as
an abbreviation.

On the results

It was with much anticipation – and a teeny bit of trepidation – that we met with Alex to discuss the results. *Golden Meaning* intentionally includes the work of a broad range of designers in terms of their specialisms, ages, backgrounds and nationalities. In selecting contributors, we were aiming for contrast and diversity. Looking for the first time at all the designs together, it was clear that our hopes had been exceeded. From the tongue-in-cheek to the profound, the figurative to the diagrammatic, the work of numerically-orientated typographers sat alongside that of lateral-thinking image-makers, with all kinds of variants in between. Contributors had employed linguistics, history, music, fashion and cookery – alongside maths of course – in order to engage and inform mathematicians and non-mathematicians alike. Accuracy was occasionally sacrificed in favour of wit or charm, but Alex was nonetheless impressed by the cleverness and skill on display. Most significantly for us, he understood the responses that we had failed to!

In the spirit of GraphicDesign&, this project makes the case for what design and designers can do, revealing the design process and making it accessible to a non-design audience. Conversely, it also attempts to demystify maths, a subject often considered baffling. Whatever your interest or level of knowledge, we hope that these 55 interpretations of the golden mean will intrigue, inform and delight.

For half a millennium, the golden mean has played as much of a role in the history of art and design as it has in science and mathematics.

When Lucienne Roberts and Rebecca Wright asked for my advice as to what maths concept would make a good subject for a design challenge, we discussed many possibilities. It became clear that the golden mean was the perfect fit, since the number already combines notions of both abstract and visual beauty.

I was fascinated to see how the designers would combine the mathematical ideas with the aesthetic ones, and I was not disappointed. The results are insightful, moving, witty, playful, stylish, clever – and refreshingly diverse. The 55 designers have interpreted elements of mathematics in areas including sculpture, cuisine, poetry, typography, cosmology and hair.

But before we get there, here's a brief guide to the golden mean. Look at the line below:

The line is separated into two sections in such a way that the ratio of the whole line to the larger section is equal to the ratio of the larger section to the smaller section. This ratio is equal to 1.618. In other words, when a line is divided in this way, the whole line is 1.618 times longer than the larger section, which is 1.618 times longer than the smaller section.

There is something very elegant about describing a number using geometry, even if the number produced looks awkward. The ancient Greeks were the first to study the golden mean, which they called the 'extreme and mean' ratio. They learned how to draw a line cut in two like the one above with a compass and a ruler. This line emerged in the construction of the five-pointed star, a sacred symbol, which established the first link between the number and mysticism.

Two millennia later, in Renaissance Italy, the number became more formally embraced by religion. The Italian mathematician Luca Pacioli wrote a book, *The Divine Proportion*, in which he claimed that the number provided a God-given template for artistic beauty. He gave no proof of this claim beyond faith and mathematical simplicity, but it was accepted by his peers, including Leonardo da Vinci, and since then the number gained its aureate synonyms: the golden mean, the golden ratio, the golden section, the golden cut and, later, φ or phi. Artists and architects began to use the golden ratio to position elements in their work.

The geometrical definition of the golden mean is an expression of perfect balance and self-containment. Let's look at one consequence of its unique geometry. Consider a rectangle where the length of one side is 1.618 times the length of the other – a shape we call a 'golden rectangle'. This shape divides perfectly into a square and a smaller golden rectangle, as illustrated below. And we can keep on dividing golden rectangles into squares and smaller golden rectangles *ad infinitum*.

  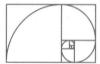

In the third image I have drawn a quarter circle in each of the squares, which link to make a spiral. Mathematically, we call this a 'logarithmic spiral', but in this case we can call it a 'golden spiral' too. One reason why there is fascination with this type of spiral is because we can see it in nature: for example, in galaxies, in the nautilus shell and in the seed heads of sunflowers.

In the late nineteenth century, the German Adolf Zeising claimed that the golden mean was a 'paramount spiritual ideal' that permeates 'all structure, forms and proportions, whether cosmic or individual, organic or inorganic, acoustic or optical; which finds its fullest realization, however, in the human form.' An outlandish claim, certainly, but it was taken seriously. If you look at the human body, there are good approximations to the golden mean: the distance between the big knuckle and the middle knuckle on a finger is roughly 1.618 times the distance from the middle to the small one.

The psychologist Gustav Fechner decided to find out which rectangle shape was most beautiful. He showed a selection of rectangles to a group of subjects and asked them to select their favourite. The golden rectangle came out top. Thus the link between the golden mean and beauty was scientifically proven, at least for the standards of the time. Even though Fechner's methodology is now regarded as flawed, the link between golden mean and beauty has been an area of serious scientific study for a century. While most academics do not believe that beauty can be summed up in a number, there remain many scholars – and plastic surgeons! – who do.

Irrespective of its aesthetic value, the golden mean is mathematically fascinating, and one way to see this is to look at its connection to the Fibonacci sequence, which is the roll call of numbers below:

0, 1, 1, 2, 3, 5, 8, 13, 21, 34, 55, 89...

In this sequence, each number is the sum of the two numbers before it. So,

$0 + 1 = 1$

$1 + 1 = 2$

$1 + 2 = 3$

$2 + 3 = 5$

and so on...

There is something very natural about the Fibonacci sequence. It seems to model natural growth, always building on what comes before, and it is the case that Fibonacci numbers appear a lot in nature. Flowers tend to have a Fibonacci number of petals, and cones, cauliflower and sunflower heads have Fibonacci numbers of spirals.

If we look at the ratio between consecutive Fibonacci numbers:

$$\frac{1}{1} \qquad \frac{2}{1} \qquad \frac{3}{2} \qquad \frac{5}{3} \qquad \frac{8}{5} \qquad \frac{13}{8} \qquad \frac{21}{13} \qquad \frac{34}{21} \qquad \frac{55}{34} \quad ...$$

which is

| 1 | 2 | 1.5 | 1.667 | 1.6 | 1.625 | 1.615 | 1.619 | 1.618 ... |

we see that the further we go down the sequence, the closer the ratio is to the golden mean.

Let's now consider the 'golden angle', 137.5°, which is the angle we get when we divide 360° into two angles such that the bigger one is 1.618 the size of the smaller one.

The golden angle presents us with one of the best examples I know of the intersection between abstract and visual beauty. Imagine a flower head produces seeds from a centre point, such that each new seed is pushed from the centre in a direction that is a rotation of 137.5° from the previous one. The following pattern is produced:

Gorgeous!

OK, that's enough maths. If you have never considered these ideas before, it's a lot to get your head around, and unless you are a bit of a geek you probably have never thought very deeply about them. To summarise: the golden mean and the Fibonacci sequence are geometrical and numerical models for 'perfect' natural growth, which have entered lay consciousness as a blueprint for beauty.

The responses to GraphicDesign&'s challenge engage with many aspects of the golden mean. Some have chosen to focus on the number itself, 1.618, covering the page with its random-looking decimal digits. Some have chosen to focus on the numbers of the Fibonacci sequence. There are many golden rectangles, golden spirals, golden angles and there is even a golden ass and some golden flapjacks.

As a popular maths writer, I am always trying to make abstract ideas accessible and fun. This book succeeds brilliantly in doing just that. I have found it incredibly refreshing to see what to me are familiar concepts reinterpreted in novel, creative ways. Even those ideas that I would have expected from graphic designers – such as typefaces, logos, wallpapers – bring out something new. I also like the way that the whole spectrum of opinions is covered – from those that take seriously the notion that the golden mean prescribes beauty to those who want to subvert it. Likewise, you get a spread from the highly abstract to the very real, from computer-generated geometrical diagrams to illustrations drawn by hand.

There are parallels between what mathematicians do and what the authors of the following pages have done. Mathematicians play around with numbers, shapes, concepts and patterns in order to prove theorems. The designers here have played around with numbers, shapes, concepts and patterns for the purposes of visual communication. Both activities are creative, but with different ends.

This book deserves attention from the maths community as much as it does the design one.

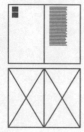

Alt Group

Dean Poole
b1970/New Zealand

www.altgroup.net

---

ink : unprinted paper =
ink + unprinted paper : unprinted paper =
ϕ

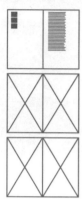

Lara Assouad Khoury
b1976/Lebanon

www.lara-assouadkhoury.com

I wanted to construct a *Golden Meaning* Arabic alphabet. Using a small golden rectangle as a module, and the diagonal defined by its opposing corners, I composed two larger golden rectangles: one vertical and the other horizontal. I drew on the rich ornamental pattern heritage in Arabic Middle Eastern art for the grid, and early Kufi manuscripts for the structure of the letterforms.

The letters fill either one or two, often overlapping, rectangles that share a square in common. This is more apparent in the three highlighted letters on the left-hand pages of my contribution.

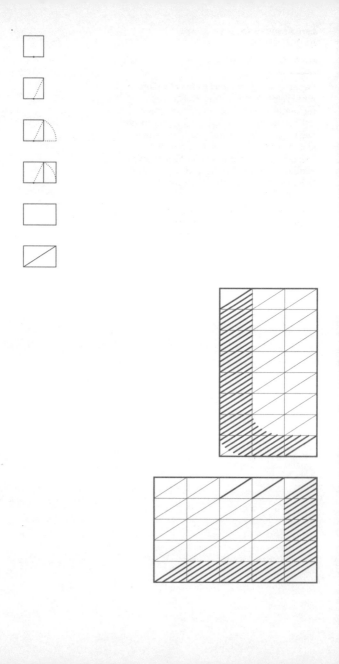

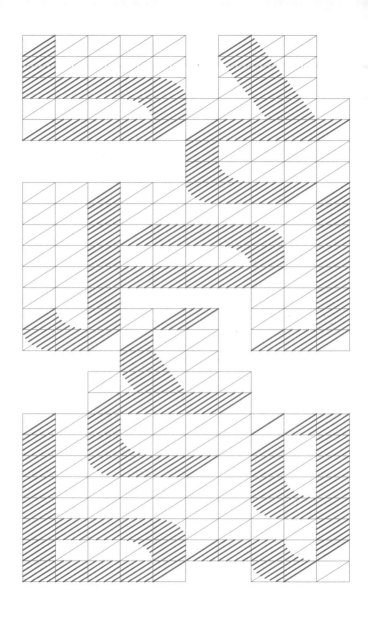

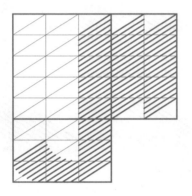

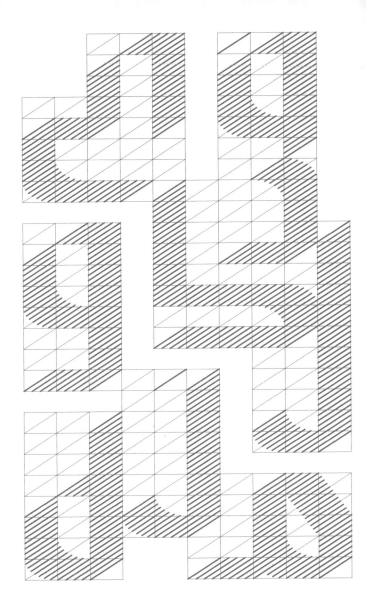

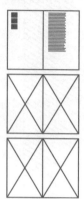

———

We were struck by how hard it is to remember the numbers associated with the golden mean. The golden ratio (1:1.618...) is described as 'irrational'. This means that it cannot be represented as a simple fraction – which doesn't make it, or any of the numbers derived from it, very memorable. The golden angle (137.508...°) is equally hard to retain.

As graphic designers we thought it would be useful to develop a visual mnemonic for both the golden ratio and the golden angle. A mnemonic is a technique for remembering complex information using association.

We took two standard objects of measurement and set them to the golden proportions. We now can't forget the results:

Golden ratio
If a 0–100°C thermometer is divided using the golden ratio the mercury would stop rising at approximately 38°C, the temperature of blood in humans.

Golden angle
If a circular clock face is divided using the golden ratio, one of the possible divisions falls at 12.23 – the alliteration and the number sequence makes it particularly pleasing and memorable.

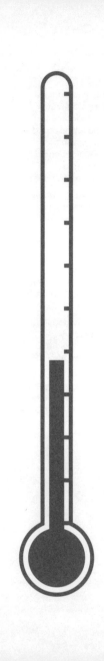

38°C

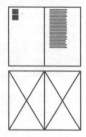

Rose Blake

b1987/UK

www.rose-blake.co.uk

—————

I started thinking about how there is only a short span of time when the relationship between the height of a parent and their child is the equivalent of the golden ratio. This occurs, on average, when a child is aged 11 – when they start secondary school, try to act like a grown-up and really begin thinking about what it means to be on this planet. It is at this point the relationship between parent and child changes, but only the parent realises this.

It's in a finger and a honey bee
The curve of a hurricane and the galaxy

And for this brief moment in our lives
The height of you and me

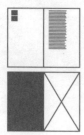

Bianca Chang
b1987/Australia

www.biancachang.com

———

I created a paper sculpture to explore whether the golden ratio is really central to beauty. An experimental and intuitive process, I took a cube of layered paper and divided it into blocks. I divided these in height or width or depth using the golden ratio. I then used the blocks to build a construction that was visually harmonious.

———

photography Jacob Ring

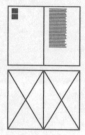

Kyuhyung Cho
b1975/Korea

www.kyuhyungcho.com

I believe that the design process is all about discovery, driven by curiosity, and that design is therefore not about producing something new entirely from scratch.

I started this project by observing my everyday life, looking for clues that could shape my design. I wanted to challenge my understanding of the golden mean, to allow time, psychology and behaviour to inform the outcome, so that my response to the brief would go beyond being only an objective interpretation.

I experimented, using the golden ratio – walking to the golden mean point between my studio and home, listening back to conversations with friends to hear what was being said at the moment of the golden mean – yet none of those efforts gave me inspiration. I continued to search for my personal relationship to the golden mean.

Looking further at my daily schedules and rhythms, I began to see a pattern emerge. Considering the day as a circle, I wondered about representing the ratio of sleep to activity as a pie chart. The result appeared close to the golden angle of 137.5–222.5°. Using the golden ratio (1:1.618), a day is divided into 14 hours 50 minutes and 9 hours 10 minutes, a pattern close to my own life of bed around 10pm and waking at 7am.

Are we designed to live according to the golden ratio? I am curious if there is more to be discovered.

14 hours 50 minutes on: 9 hours 10 minutes off
A Day in My Life

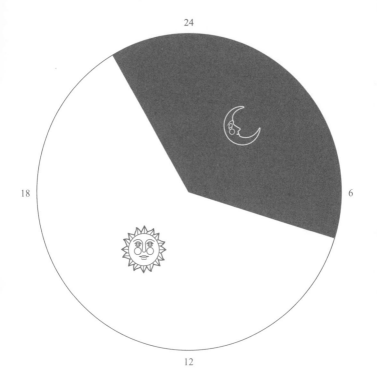

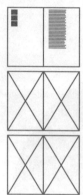

Peter Crawley
b1985/UK

www.petercrawley.co.uk

For many centuries architects, designers and artists have used the Fibonacci sequence, phi and the golden ratio in their work – some knowingly, some purely coincidentally.

My design references architecture, phi and the Fibonacci sequence at every opportunity. Both the forms and the spaces between them have been constructed using values derived from the Fibonacci sequence and the value of phi.

When the height of each rectangle is divided by its width, the resulting number gets increasingly close to the value of phi the nearer you get to the rectangle at the centre of the spread. Interestingly, various chance relationships between geometry and negative space relating to phi and the Fibonacci sequence also started appearing through the design process – the height difference between successive blocks, for example, and the diagonals running across the blocks.

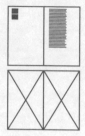

Fred Deakin
b1964/UK

www.freddeak.in

I've applied the golden mean to an isometric projection of expanded cubes, with each of their elements and various sizes scaled in proportion to one another. As I hoped, several pleasing geometric coincidences have emerged as a result: the golden ratio seems to endlessly reproduce itself given half a chance!

I had a geeky passion for recreational mathematics as a boy, fuelled by the books of the late great American columnist Martin Gardner, and it's always satisfying when I use the same skills I discovered back then to generate pattern-based material for my graphic and musical work. All hail Fibonacci and the golden ratio!

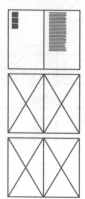

deskcamping

Nick Couch
b1973/UK

www.deskcamping.com

———

Coming up with the idea to do 'golden bars' wasn't the biggest of creative leaps. I was reading Alex Bellos's *Alex's Adventures in Numberland* while watching *The Great British Bake Off* on TV. A happy coincidence. One eye on a page with lots of '$F \times F = F \times F - 1$' and the other on a rather perky macaroon. I'd just about managed to get my head around the repetition of 1.6... something... something... and wondered if the recurring nature of the golden ratio could be applied to ingredients.

You'll notice that the recipe for golden bars doesn't have any measurements. My theory is, if you understand the principle you can often get to an approximate answer, nine times out of 10. For example, $A + B$ = roughly C, or 6,700 divided by 3, roughly 2,233. Umm, let me check. Yeah, sort of.

When it comes to maths, I'm more of a feeler. I can usually land the ball on the green. Whether it's near the hole is another matter. I think we're all a bit like that. The same thing applies here. If you understand the recurring proportions of the golden ratio you can ditch your weighing scales.

Forget numbers, feel the ratio.

butter

sugar

syrup

sultanas

oats

golden bars

1. set the oven to 160°C
2. melt the butter in a saucepan
3. add the sugar and syrup to the melted butter to heat through
4. remove from the heat and stir in the oats and sultanas
5. spread the mixture into a well greased shallow tin
6. bake for about 20 minutes or until golden
7. remove from the oven and mark into bars while still warm

leave to cool

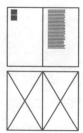

Europa

Mia Frostner
b1980/Sweden

Robert Sollis
b1981/UK

Paul Tisdell
b1982/UK

www.europaeuropa.co.uk

If Fibonacci was a concrete poet.

RATIO

MULTIPLY

A I

TO SEE

EXPONENTIALLY

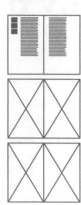

Face37

Rick Banks
b1985/UK

www.face37.com

Tom Duncalf
b1985/UK

www.tomduncalf.com

Our primary inspiration was the relationship between the mathematical simplicity and elegance of the Fibonacci sequence and the complexity found in nature described by the sequence – for example in the number of seeds in the head of a sunflower or the spirals around the outside of a pineapple.

We combined our individual specialisations of typography and software development and created a piece of interactive software that uses the Fibonacci sequence to process and distort typography, in this case a quote from the film *Pi*; 'Mathematics is the language of nature'.

The software, developed using Processing (www.processing.org), takes the typographic layout and splits the outline of each letter into thousands of individual points. These points are then systematically joined together in all possible combinations. Each letter is then assigned an index number, which we then used to identify a number in the Fibonacci sequence. So, for example, a letter with an index of 10 would correspond to the 10th number in the Fibonacci sequence, 34.

The same number of lines to the allocated Fibonnaci number are then randomly selected from the set of all possible lines and joined together, also randomly. Those letters that were assigned Fibonacci numbers at the beginning of the sequence are only suggested as forms, while those that corresponded to high value numbers are visually dense, with lines spilling outside of their outline form.

The software allowed us to explore different combinations of index numbers and to recalculate each letter as required, and the final design (one of an infinite number of possible outputs) uses an increasing number of lines for each letter, starting with the index number 8 (21 lines) and ending with 15 (610 lines), to hint at the evolving complexity of nature.

An interactive version of the software used to create the design is available at www.languageofnature.co.uk.

untitled

```
48      thi
49
50      this
51      for(
52        PV
53        sh
54      }
55      this
56
57      this
58    }
59
60    void d
61      this
62
63      for
64        PV
65        fo
66
67
68
69
70
71
72
73
74
75
76
77
78
79
80
81
82
83
84
85
86
87        }
88      }
89    }
90
91    boolean testLine(int intersectCount, PVector v, PVec
```

t_final

Settings

FREQ IN CHAMBERS

7   12
7   12   LETTERS
8   13   12   72
8   13   TRANSLATE X   TRANSLATE Y
9   14   7   0.5
9   14   START   SCALE
10   SET
10   255
11   OPACITY
11   0.4   0.4
    CONTROL 1   CONTROL 2
    RECALC
    HOLD   UPDATE
    PDF
    ANIMATE   255

Spaces: 2   Processing

) {

LANGUAGE

NATURE

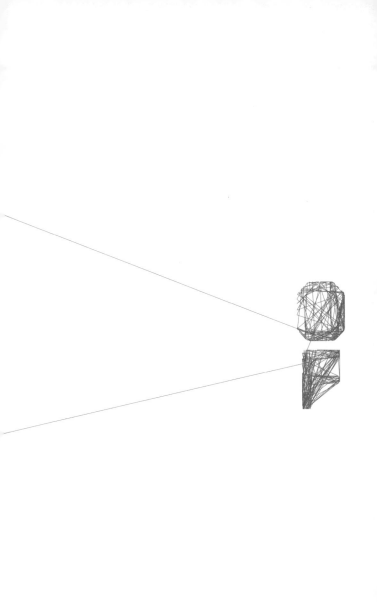

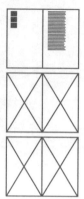

Malika Favre
b1982/France
www.malikafavre.com

———

I decided to approach the brief as
I remember approaching mathematical
exercises in high school, setting strict
constraints and rules before moving on
to the more instinctive part of the process.
As a starting point, I constructed a strict
golden ratio grid within the double page
spread without thinking about what
I wanted to draw or how I would draw it.
Once the grid was finished, I looked at what
the lines were showing and saw a silhouette
emerging. I started drawing shapes and
lines as an overlay, using the lines and angles
of the grid as a loose guide but relying on
my instinct to create what became a woman
walking by.

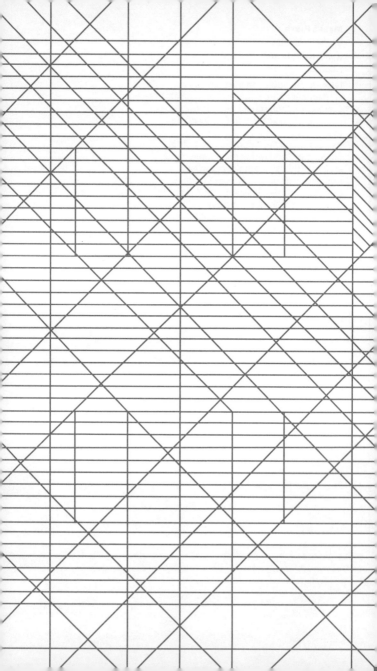

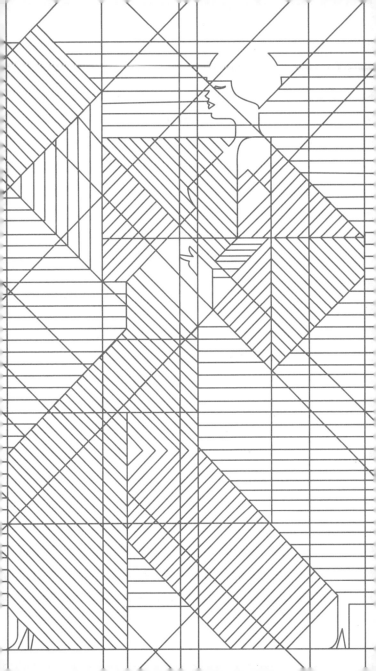

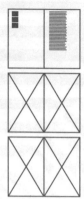

António Felizardo
b1983/Portugal

antoniofelizardo@me.com

In architecture, sculpture, painting, music... for many centuries, the golden mean has been applied as a basis for creative work. Despite its prevalence both in art and the natural world, it seems to remain somewhat abstract, filed away in a cabinet of curiosities that are part of our classical past – its relationship to the digitised world relatively unexplored.

Just like the irrational golden mean, to the uninitiated the representation of digital signals might look random and unorganised. I was interested in mapping one on to the other to see what they produce. Taking this as my starting point, I worked with two images of famous examples of ancient Greek sculpture – the *Venus de Milo* and a Diadumenos torso – and opened them in a text editor. This revealed a long series of seemingly accidental letters and numbers that made up the architecture of the file. I picked out every number and, through a long process of find and replace, paired them with numbers in the Fibonacci sequence. I then saved the files and got the images shown on the two left-hand pages of my contribution. This experiment in how earlier means of producing visual perfection might be applied in a contemporary, digitised way leaves remnants of the original pieces visible. The resultant images, although heavily distorted, are still beautiful and intriguing. The two remaining pages of my contribution show the results in detail.

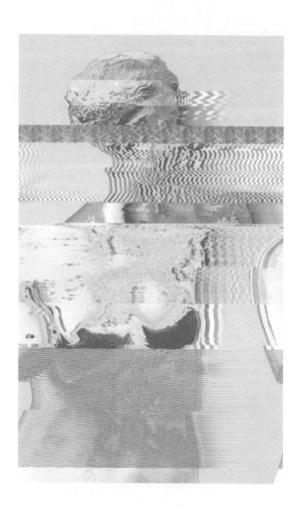

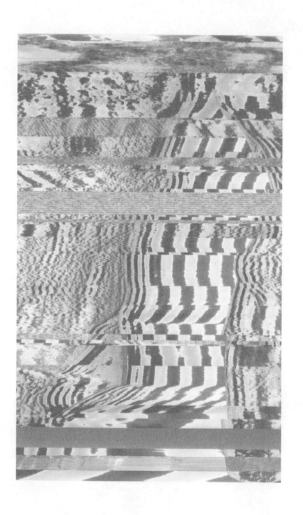

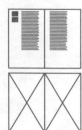

FL@33

Tomi Vollauschek
b1973/Austria

www.flat33.com

My design combines three different explorations of the golden ratio placed on top of one another, to create an intricate graphic piece that shows the versatility and wonder of the golden mean.

The golden ratio is expressed as 1:1.618... However, this is an irrational number as it runs to an infinite number of decimal places. The background to my design includes the golden ratio decimal number to 10,000 decimal places.

The proportions of a single page of this book make it a golden rectangle. My design compares three different approaches to page layout and grid structures in book design. Each rectangle represents a block of text positioned on a golden section page. The inner rectangle on the left-hand page shows designer Jan Tschichold's 'golden canon of page construction'. The inner rectangle on the right-hand page shows the van de Graaf canon, originated by Dutch book design scholar, JA van de Graaf.

Both are placed within a further rectangle, mirrored from left- to right-hand page. These two show the position of the text area often used in medieval books. One of the interesting aspects of the golden rectangle is that it can be drawn purely geometrically, without using measurements. The positions of the text areas shown are all arrived at geometrically and the various intersections included in my design highlight how they interrelate. According to the designers cited, these proportions produce some of the most harmonious page layouts possible.

If you are drawing a golden rectangle geometrically, you start by drawing a right angle and an arc to arrive at a square. I have used these forms to create a spiral on each of my pages that approximates the golden spiral. Alongside this, the circular elements in my design use a Fibonacci spiral multiplied and rotated using the golden angle of 137.5°. It has been rotated 144 times at this angle because it is only after this point that the original spiral is repeated. Unsurprisingly, 144 is a Fibonacci number.

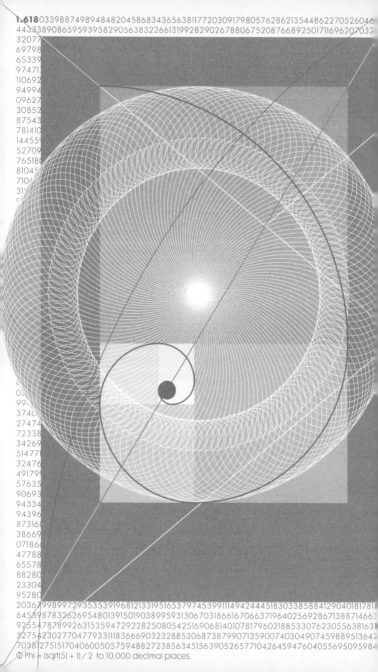

1.6180339887498948482045868343656381177203091798057628621354486227052604
4433389086595939582905638322661319928290267880675208766892501711696207032

32077
69798
65339
97471
110692
94994
09627
30852
87543
781410
144559
52709
765180
81045
71043
31?
?

03
99-
37409
27474
72338
34269
514771
32476
49179?
57635
90693
94334
94396
873168
38669
071866
47788
65578
88280
23304
95280

20367999899729353539196812133195165379745399111494244451830338588412904018178
645599878326269548013915019038995931306703186661670663719640256928671388714663
92554787899263153594729228250805425169068140107817960218853307623055638163
3275423027704779331118366690323288530687387990713590074030490745988951364
70381275151704060050575948827238563451563905265771042645947604055695095988
Φ Phi = (sqrt(5) + 1) / 2 to 10,000 decimal places.

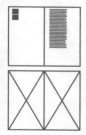

Melvin Galapon
b1981/UK

www.mynameismelvin.co.uk

––––––––

A single page of this book is a golden
rectangle. This was the starting point for
my design. I wanted to keep my idea as
pure as possible, using all the available
space on the page. I divided a double page
spread into a grid where I placed a series
of smaller golden rectangles. I worked
out the dimensions of each to ensure the
entire page was filled with these rectangles
and then adjusted the opacity of each
of them to diminish in line with the golden
mean. So, the first was filled with 100%
of pure colour, the next was a 62% tint
(100 ÷ 1.618), then 38% (62 ÷ 1.618) and
so on until eventually the last rectangle in
the series appears not to be filled with any
colour at all.

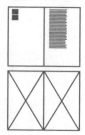

George Hardie
b1944/UK

www.a-g-i.org/member-work/work/204

I made a decision to translate the golden mean into three dimensions and work with volume.

The drawing was made just after pouring out three equal amounts of wine and re-corking the bottle. The wine is a golden Sauterne, Chateau d'Yquem 1970, bought in that year, with my first salary cheque, from Mr Harcourt at the Army and Navy Stores in London. (This memory may contain traces of the truth.) The three different glasses have been invented for the project.

Optimistically, the bottle remains more than half full. There are 463ml left in the 750ml bottle (1.61803... wine:1. space). The wine poured leaves the glasses more than half full with 96ml in each of their different shapes and equal volumes (1.61803... wine:1. space). The cork is optimistically left more than half out of the bottle. (1. in:1.61803... out.)

Turning from mathematical accuracy to aesthetics and taste, Chateau d'Yquem is unexpectedly considered the perfect match/balance for foie gras, blue cheese and strawberries.

After dealing with volume and three dimensions, I turned to the fourth dimension. Time is represented by the clock face divided into the perfect proportion of time spent between thinking and making, or drawing and doing sums.

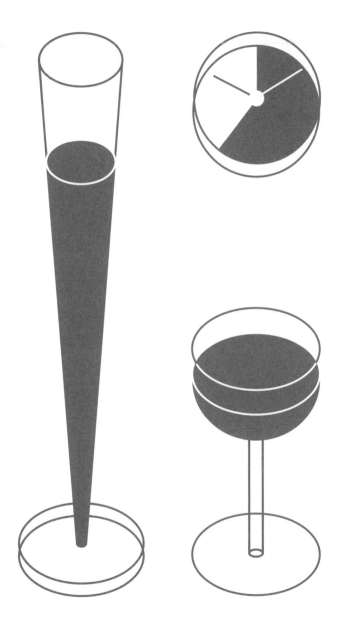

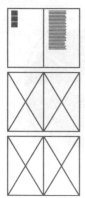

Julia Hasting
b1970/Germany

www.juliahasting.com

All three of my drawings are based on
a circle expanding in size according to the
golden ratio. The first image shows a drop
falling, the second its ripples seen from
above. In each the circle increases in size,
with the relationship of smaller to larger
determined by the golden ratio. I used the
circles' diameter to make these calculations.
The 'foam' is made out of multiples of all
the circles previously shown as ripples.
So, if you were to centre these circles one
on top of the other you would see the ripple
image once more.

From micro to macro, the golden ratio
manifests itself most harmoniously when
applied to this most perfect shape, the circle.
I like to think of this as a golden drop. It falls.
It ripples the surface and then multiplies into
golden foam. The connections between the
golden ratio, movement and time create
beautiful visual relationships between these
many circular forms.

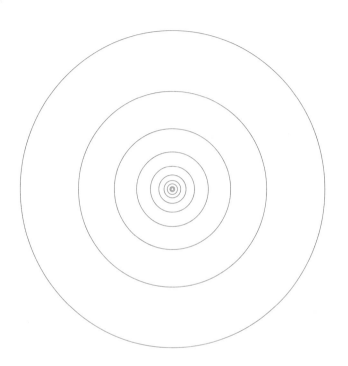

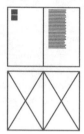

Homework

Jerzy Skakun
b 1973 / Poland

Joanna Górska
b 1976 / Poland

www.facebook.com/HomeworkDesign
www.homework.com.pl

———

When we were asked to participate in this project, my first thought was of my grandfather who passed away a few years ago. He was a maths fanatic. I remembered his desk drawer where there were rulers, squares, callipers, protractors, pencils and a rubber. My grandfather and I would often play and draw circles and weird' geometric figures. I did not follow my grandfather and become a mathematician. However, I have found there is a lot of maths in graphics, especially in vector design.

Mindful of the Renaissance notion that the golden ratio is 'divine' and the secret of true beauty, I wanted to check this out. I drew a logarithmic spiral and found that this beautiful shape is used to depict many beautiful things: hair curls, shells, etc. I flipped these elements and repeated them, noticing that the mirrored spiral created the shape of an idealised apple, which when rotated, became the ideal ass – I have used maths to depict ideal beauty, albeit a little obscene! Mathematical perfection becomes a perversion. The letters for the title are also based on this logarithmic spiral.

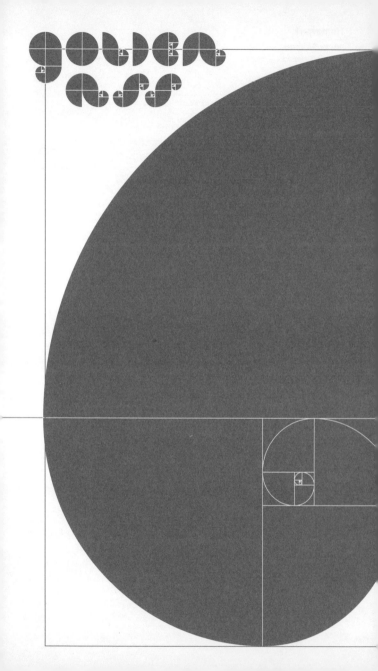

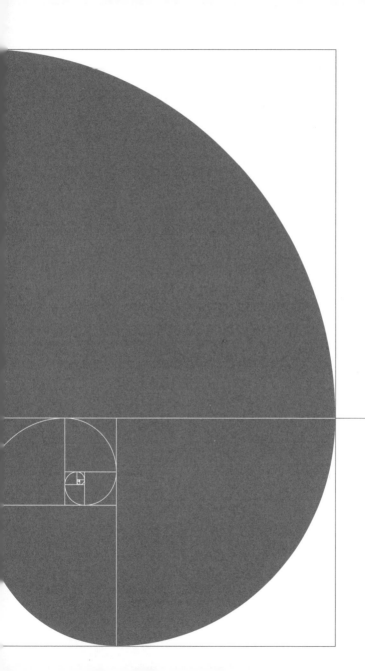

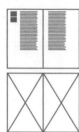

Hort

www.hort.org.uk

———

'Times of the predominance of rectangular fields in cattle husbandry are definitely over' states Ron Garner, agriculturalist and initiator of the campaign Rethink the Field. Garner presses for an aesthetic awareness among cultivators. With reference to Leonardo da Vinci's *Vitruvian Man* and Le Corbusier's Modulor, he postulates to drag the living thing back into focus. 'When it comes to defining fields most cultivators blindly follow the boundaries of their realties. Driven by the intent of making the most of given space they create mostly unharmonious structures which do not relate to the proportions and aesthetic preferences of animals. Cattle are being put on to fields in an ignorant this-is-it-live-with-it manner.'

According to the agricultural innovator, this insensitive approach denies cattle's inherent sensibility for aesthetics. This results in decreased animal well-being, which ultimately shows up in inferior product quality – a problem Garner is eager to solve: 'Fuelled by today's knowledge, scientific insight and technology we now have a great opportunity to change the game. Owing to my concept of Aesthetic Agriculture we are finally able to iron out the massive mistakes which have been made since the very beginning of husbandry. By rethinking the basic idea of the field and tweaking fields in witty, golden and precise ways we can raise this agricultural sector to the next level.'

Garner's concept is based on the golden spiral and supported by high-precision laser measurement technology. Critics bemoan the whole concept, saying it is just about setting up fences in a spiral-like shape, wasting resources like land, wire, time and money. In addition, they repeatedly label Garner as 'golden windbag' and the whole idea as an esoteric farce. Utterances such as 'nobody needs chewy steaks and bland-tasting milk. They are things of the past!' may sound populist, but Garner gets backing from the authorities. A series of field experiments conducted within the context of an early 2013 Department for Rural Affairs study prove 'a variety of undeniably positive effects induced by the innovative agricultural approach of Mr Ron Garner'.

Cattle reared in so-called 'golden fields' that comply with the requirements of Garner's conceptual idea of Aesthetic Agriculture show a distinct rise in happiness hormones in comparison to cattle reared on a regular field – a fact to which Garner keeps referring, claiming he has 'up to 87% happier cattle'. Moreover, the golden field test group was less prone to inflammations and other diseases, the meat structure was more delicate and the milk had increased flavour. One cow from the golden field group won the first prize in a beauty competition, whereas none of the other test group were nominated.

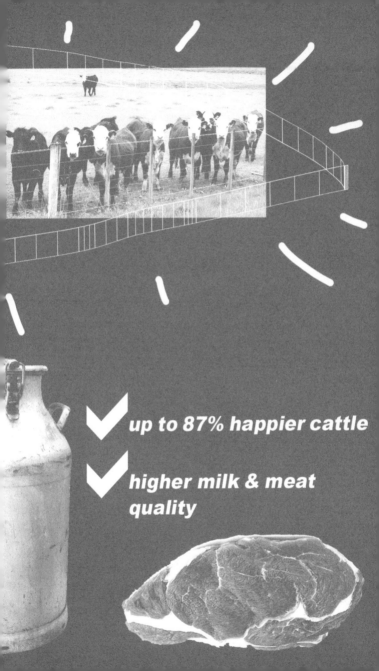

up to 87% happier cattle

higher milk & meat quality

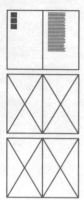

Mark Hudson
b1961/UK

www.markhudson.net

We are surrounded by beautiful rectangles
in the UK. They just feel right to us. Beyond
doubt, pleasing, satisfactory, permanent.
But where does this 'rightness' reside? Have
we been bludgeoned by their very familiarity?
Or do they conform to some over-arching
aesthetic law? And what would happen
to their rightness if they were redesigned to
adhere strictly to golden ratio proportions?

In the 1880s, German philosopher and
experimental psychologist Gustav Fechner
ran an experiment, testing a range of
rectangles for pleasing proportion. This
is reworked and extended here to look
at our current surroundings. It throws
up intriguing issues and some uneasy
neighbours emerge – a Kindle Fire and
a Penguin paperback have almost identical
proportions. Data storage formats seem
to congregate, as passports, SD cards
and *The Sun* share a row. Some classic
gambles stick together; cigarette packets
and dominoes. And look for class-based
clusters of shapes if you dare.

The various forms are clearly dictated by
function, manufacture, usage, handling and
a host of other drivers. And variety works.
We are also peering down on ourselves:
looking at a visual diary of our time, like
Voyager 1's Golden Record launched into
space in 1977, but magnificently mundane
and shot through with a hunger for
stimulation and instantaneity. Twenty,
even 10 years ago, this time capsule would
have looked very different. Are our lives
really the sum of these rectangles?

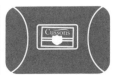

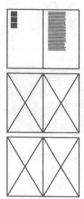

Ibán Ramón + Dídac Ballester

Ibán Ramón
b1969/Spain

Dídac Ballester
b1972/Spain

www.ibanmasdidac.com

Our intention was to experiment with
the golden ratio three-dimensionally, and
play not only with volumes but also with
voids. We commissioned Ricardo Alcaide
to manufacture a set of wooden blocks
based on the Fibonacci sequence
(0, 1, 1, 2, 3, 5, 8, 13). Eight wooden blocks
3 x 3 x 3cm, five wooden blocks 6 x 6 x 6cm,
three wooden blocks 9 x 9 x 9cm and two
wooden blocks 15 x 15 x 15cm. The most
important thing in this exercise is that both
the blocks and the empty spaces are built
on a grid based on the Fibonacci sequence,
so are related to the golden ratio. The result
is a collection of more than 50 different
compositions, each with a real harmony
between volume and void.

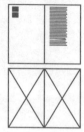

Julia

Valerio Di Lucente
b1981/Italy

Erwan Lhuissier
b1983/France

Hugo Timm
b1981/Brazil

www.julia.uk.com

Like Mr Levin in the extract from Alex Bellos's book sent with the brief, we have focused our attention on the quest to find the Fibonacci sequence in the world around us. Our interest was in superimposing the Fibonacci sequence on to something that already exists to see what this might produce.

We chose language as our subject and asked ourselves: what would happen if we matched the sequence with the entire *Oxford English Dictionary* (OED) online? On the OED website, every one of the 272,858 words is assigned a number. We ran the sequence as far as it would go before running out of words. Our last possible entry is word number 196,418. We had no pretension that by doing this experiment we would reveal any particular truth – we were motivated by intellectual curiosity.

We enjoyed the synchronicity of this idea too – while working on the project we were struck by the connection between the title of this book, *Golden Meaning,* and a dictionary as a definitive record of meaning.

We have set the text in Pacioli, a redrawing of Luca Pacioli's 1509 alphabet of 'divine proportion', so this outcome might also be viewed as a type specimen.

A [1]

A [2]

A [3]

A [5]

A– [8]

A– [13]

AALENIAN [21]

AARONITE [34]

ABACKWARD [55]

ABANDONEDLY [89]

ABATING [144]

ABDUCENS [233]

ABIOLOGICAL [377]

Fibonacci &
Oxford English Dictionary

ABOUNDINGLY [610]

ABUSEMENT [987]

ACERBATE [1597]

ADAR [2584]

AFFIRMED [4181]

ALLOCUTE [6765]

A'PERE [10946]

BAN [17711]

BURGLAR [28657]

CORPORALITY [46368]

FAWNERY [75025]

MADBRAIN [121393]

RELEVEL [196418]

Online Edition
[Accessed 14th April 2013]

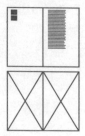

Christopher Jung
b 1975/Germany

www.studio-jung.com

———

The golden mean (gm) is everywhere
and nowhere… meaning; while it is nice to
have the gm to create pleasing proportions,
there are still many things that are beautiful
that have little connection to the gm.
I thought of something really beautiful,
which has no apparent relation to the gm –
cloud formations.

Given that the format of this book is a golden
rectangle, I fitted these cloud formations
into the geometrical framework that defines
the text area on a classical page, according
to van de Graaf's canon.

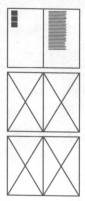

Our four designs are abstract interpretations of a Fibonacci spiral. The underlying grid uses squares that increase in size according to the Fibonacci sequence 1, 1, 2, 3, 5, 8, 13, 21 and 34. In each design, the squares are filled by a character from our Geometric pattern font collection. Each geometric font character fills a square, which means that they have the perfect dimensions to scale easily in these experiments.

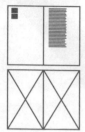

Keller Maurer Design
Germany

www.km-d.com

In our daily design practice we tend to ignore the principles of the golden section – although we might be subconsciously applying its aesthetics since it's something that seems to hold the world together.

After quite a bit of research into the meaning of the golden mean, we found ourselves slightly overwhelmed by the extensiveness of the subject. At the same time, we had the impression that all of these illustrations of sections, rectangles and spirals have been seen far too often.

We thought we would offer some practical advice: how to peel a pineapple. This is a real trick some readers might have never heard about and it very much relates to the golden mean(ing).

The pineapple in numbers

Eating and relishing a pineapple never goes without that certain pang caused by tiny stingers embedded in the sweet flesh underneath the eyes.

Here is what to do if you want to savour this tropical delight without pain:

Lay your pineapple on its side and chop off head and bottom. Place it upright and proceed to cut off the skin, leading the knife directly under the surface from top to bottom. Once you've worked your way around and all of the skin has been removed, brown eyes will appear. Lay the fruit on its side once again and use your knife to draw a line along the eyes. Cut diagonally from both sides under the eyes and remove the triangular slices — and with them the little stingers.

The ovaries of a pineapple develop into berries which grow into a large fruit. These berries are arranged in two interlocking helices, eight in one direction, 13 in the other, each of which is a Fibonacci number.

Preparing a pineapple in the way described will result in a beautifully cut fruit with either eight or 13 helices, depending on whether you are right- or left-handed.

Bon appetit!

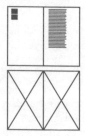

Oli Kellett
b1983/UK

www.olikellett.com

They say beauty is in the eye of the beholder, but something as subjective as beauty can be measured mathematically.

The golden ratio is a geometric proportion regarded as the key to creating aesthetically pleasing art. The golden ratio has long been used as a way of creating portraits that are more aesthetically pleasing to the eye.

In 2001, Dr Stephen R Marquardt, a retired oral surgeon from UCLA, devised a face template that used the golden ratio to define how a beautiful face should look. If your face fits this template, you are officially beautiful.

By using his mask, I created a mathematically aesthetically 'beautiful' portrait of myself. Using retouching techniques more common to a cosmetic commercial, I moved elements of my face around so that they conform to Dr Marquardt's template.

I know which one I prefer...

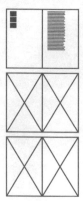

Na Kim
b1979/South Korea

www.ynkim.com
www.tableunion.com

———

In the process of researching the golden
ratio, I happened upon some criticism
of it as a formula for beauty. Then, I looked
at the paper on my table, which is mostly
A4 and A3. What about the proportions
of A-sized papers (the international standard:
ISO 216) that play such a big part in daily
life, especially for graphic designers,
office workers and all home printer users?
This proportion has become a kind of rule,
a much-used structure and a default format,
without ever claiming 'I am beauty'.

I created a series of tables that correspond
to the sizes of the A-series: A4, A3, A2, A1
and A0, which I believe are perfectly suited
to the human form. Depending on the
context, this modular system is surely just
as beautiful and flexible as any derived from
the golden mean.

———

photography LESS

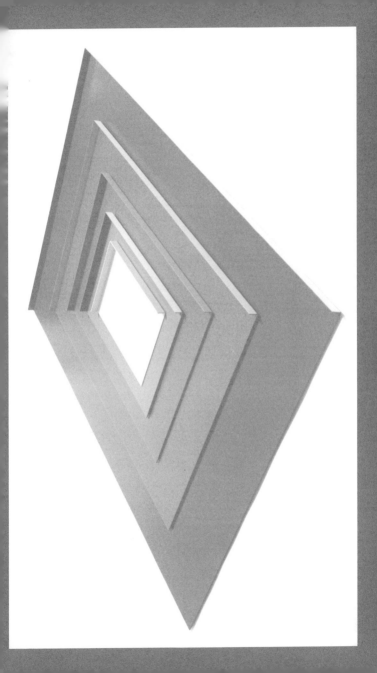

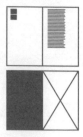

Alan Kitching
b1940/UK
www.thetypographyworkshop.com

I first understood mathematics in relation to design through working with typographer Anthony Froshaug in the 1960s and I have used the Fibonacci number sequence in various works since.

My typographic experiment is based upon the observation that, if you treat fi as a ligature, the word 'Fibonacci' has eight characters, which is a number in the Fibonacci sequence.

I set the word Fibonacci once, in 72pt Caslon italic metal type. I then moved each character horizontally by adding 1pt + 2pt + 3pt + 5pt, etc, according to the Fibonacci sequence, and took a pull on my Vandercook press each time. I then moved the whole word vertically in multiples of 12pt pica ems using the same sequence. This combination of horizontal and vertical movement, using letterpress 'furniture' and quads, suggests growth and evolving form.

fibonacci

fibonacci

fibonacci

fibonacci

fibonacci

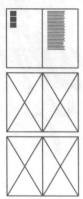

Elisabeth Kopf
b1963/Austria
www.elisabethkopf.com

There are many examples of the golden ratio in space, mathematics and organic life. What about time? Aren't space and time a continuum? Shouldn't it be possible to find the golden ratio in the dimension of time when there is obvious proof of it in the dimension of space?

I decided to investigate the unit of time that I know best: the day. Knowing that I wouldn't be able to analyse and interpret my field scientifically or theoretically, I chose to design a map that shows on which days the length of daytime and night-time correspond to the golden ratio. The internet website sunrise-sunset.dusk-dawn.com offered a very helpful tool to search for forthcoming 'golden days and nights' over the next seven years.

Alongside the longitudes of 0°, 90°, 180° and 270° I used this site to travel from the North Pole to the South Pole, looking for regions where no 'golden days and nights' occur at all, where most occur and where they occur in between. When I was sure I had collected enough data, I drew the map. What it doesn't show is that in the extreme north and south the 'golden days and nights' seem to whirl around the poles.

Golden Days & Nights...

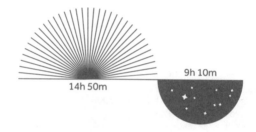

14h 50m

9h 10m

... the *Golden Ratio* of *24 hours* ...

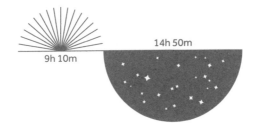

14h 50m

9h 10m

... on *Planet Earth* ...

Latitude 90°
Zero ***Golden Days & Nights***

Latitude 89°
One ***Golden Day & Night*** every few years

Latitude 42°01′
Maximum number of ***Golden Days & Nights*** ❷
Climax = 9–11 days in series:
December (16), (17), 18, 19, 20, 21, 22, 23, 24, 25, (26)

Latitude 37°92′
Maximum number of ***Golden Days & Nights*** ❶
Climax = 11–12 days in series:
June (15), 16, 17, 18, 19, 20, 21, 22, 23, 24, 25, (26), (27)

Latitude 38° to -38°
Zero ***Golden Days & Nights***

Latitude -37°92′
Maximum number of ***Golden Days & Nights*** ❶
Climax = 10–11 days in series:
December (15), (16), 17, 18, 19, 20, 21, 22, 23, 24, 25, (26), (27)

Latitude -42°01′
Maximum number of ***Golden Days & Nights*** ❷
Climax = 11–12 days in series:
June (15), 16, 17, 18, 19, 20, 21, 22, 23, 24, 25, (26), (27)

Latitude -89°
One ***Golden Day & Night*** every few years

Latitude -90°
Zero ***Golden Days & Nights***

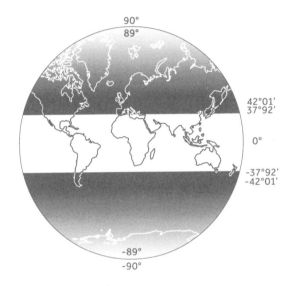

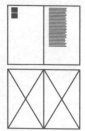

Zigmunds Lapsa
b1982/Latvia

www.zigmundslapsa.com

My design is a decorative pattern and
a word puzzle at the same time. It consists
of a pattern, constructed using the golden
ratio, which I used to lay out text in a playful
manner. I thought it appropriate, given
the special properties of the golden mean,
to use the word GROWTH as the basis of
my design.

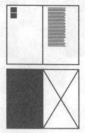

Nathalie Lees
b1970/UK

Before settling on the 'rabbits' idea, I spent a lot of time researching other ways of illustrating the golden ratio. Given how often it recurs in both design and nature, there was no shortage of inspiration to draw upon: I thought about everything from the spiralling pattern of sunflower seeds to the simple geometric shapes that you can create from it. I looked online, and found an old episode of BBC Radio 4's *In Our Time* podcast dedicated to Fibonnaci numbers, which proved particularly useful (you can download it for free).

The more research I did, the more I realised that what really caught my imagination is the way the golden ratio manifests itself in the natural world. And for a formula that seems to possess almost mystical qualities, I liked that fact that Leonardo of Pisa (Fibonnaci) developed this mathematical sequence to demonstrate something as mundane as the hypothetical breeding patterns of rabbits.

'A certain man had one pair of rabbits together in a certain enclosed space,' he wrote in 1202. 'And one wishes to know how many are created from the pair in one year, when it is the nature of them in a single month to bear another pair, and in the second month, those born to also bear.'

With this pattern set, what follows is a spiralling number of imaginary 13th-century Italian rabbits. And just as imaginary rabbits were an effective and fun way of Leonardo of Pisa explaining his theory, they also seemed to me to be a good way of solving the brief. It married the elements of mathematics and the natural world in the way I wanted. The basic construction of the final illustration is made up of circles that are proportionately 1.618 or phi – the golden ratio – to each other.

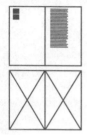

Margot Lombaert
b1988/France

www.margotlombaert.com

———

For centuries the golden ratio has fascinated mankind. The spiral pattern of a sunflower head, the body features of a blue angelfish, a nautilus shell and many works of art share the divine proportion. From Leonardo da Vinci's *Vitruvian Man* to the Braun Aromaster coffee maker, much artistic endeavour is governed by this proportion, either by design or by intuition. Where does this universal sense of harmony come from? Could our instinctive relationship to the golden ratio be linked to the origin of life itself?

Perhaps the earliest appearance of the golden ratio was at the moment of the Big Bang – a geometric analysis of our galaxy reveals the shape of a logarithmic spiral. This spiral, which forms the basis of my design, was named *spira mirabilis* (miraculous spiral) by prominent 17th-century mathematician Jacob Bernoulli, because it retains its proportion as it grows. This growth pattern has been described as 'the essential process of life'.

Intrinsically linked to so many facets of our existence, could it be that the psychological resonance of the golden ratio is because it is fundamental to who we are and why we are here?

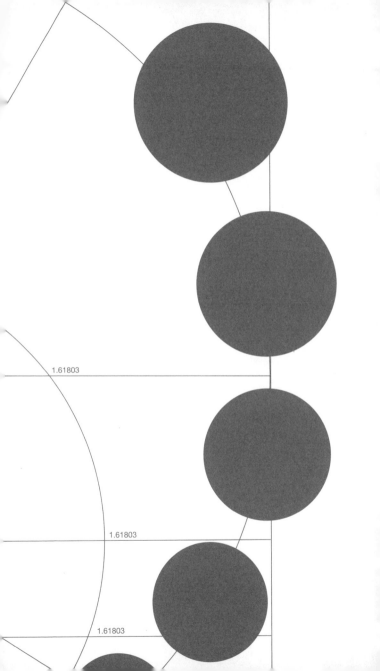

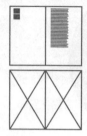

MGMT. design

Alicia Cheng
b1970/USA

Sarah Gephart
b1970/USA

www.mgmtdesign.com

As a studio, we love process and systems.
When presented with this brief we wanted
to focus on the Fibonacci sequence and how
this could be transposed on to a different
system. As an experiment, we used the Latin
alphabet to map letters on to the Fibonacci
sequence. This produced a series of two-,
three- and four-letter memes.

This series of nonsensical letter pairings
felt more like a Scrabble exercise than
any manifestation of beauty. But when we
began linking these whimsical and enigmatic
phrases, we found poetry began to emerge.

We decided to pair this infinite letter
sequence with a contemporary and finite
one: Twitter. Working within the 140-
character limit, we created a 'golden tweet'
consisting of the phrases created by using
our Fibonacci alphabet system.

We would like to invite others to submit
their own versions: crowdsourcing will make
this process infinite.

FIBONACCI NUMBERS /

1 1 2 3 5 8 13 21 34 55 89 144 233 377

ALPHABET WITH CORRESPONDING NUMBERS /

A	B	C	D	E	F	G
1	2	3	4	5	6	7

H	I	J	K	L	M	N
8	9	10	11	12	13	14

O	P	Q	R	S	T	U
15	16	17	18	19	20	21

V	W	X	Y	Z
22	23	24	25	26

FIBONACCI ALPHABET /

a	b	c	e	h	m	u	cd	ee	hi
1	2	3	5	8	13	21	34	55	89

add	bcc	cgg
144	233	377

Hi mum...
Ah, a beach!
Each bee a beau
hue! A chub
chum came 2
ace. 'Cue me a
ham, add a mac.
Be a chum, add a
cha-cha 2 me cd.
#hubbahubba!

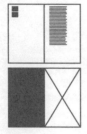

Mike Perry Studio
b1981/USA

www.mikeperrystudio.com

———

Math Rules Everything Around Me:
M. R. E. A. M.

I am not a math guy. I love and believe
in its power. I understand that it is one of the
layers in the universe that guilds existence.
I respect it. We coexist.

In my eyes, the power of a golden rectangle
comes from the organic relationships that
can fill the space it creates – the human error,
the chaos making the order function.

This is what happens on a piece of
perfect paper.

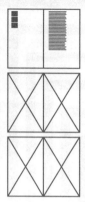

Moniker

The Netherlands

www.studiomoniker.com

On the following pages, you'll be looking Moniker in the eye: the right one belongs to Roel Wouters and the left to Luna Maurer. You see our eyes through our eyes. Eyes are often described as mirrors to the soul. Here, however, the mirror is shattered. Our eyes observe only fragments of reality, a reality that we experience nonetheless as whole. Similarly, photos are often presented as objective representations, whereas in reality they are ruptured interpretations.

Reflecting the fragmentary nature of perception and photography, we cut our pictures into shards using our Arti Flyer Tool, which we developed in collaboration with Jochem van der Spek for a series of flyers for the Amsterdam-based art society Arti et Amicitiae. We wanted to explore a classical notion of beauty via contemporary technology, so this digital tool makes it possible for users to click on predetermined lines to divide images into geometric facets that comply with the golden ratio. As the image is increasingly cut into smaller fragments, the ratio that determines where the cuts can be made stays the same. The possibilities are endless – horizontal, vertical and diagonal lines combine to form intricate kaleidoscopic patterns or to form what appear to be random divisions (see the next spread). The results, which may appear chaotic, invite us to question the supposedly harmonious qualities of the golden ratio.

---

www.arti.nl/tentoonstellingen_agenda.php

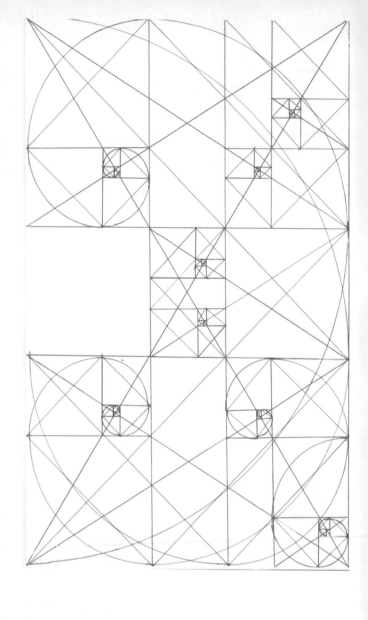

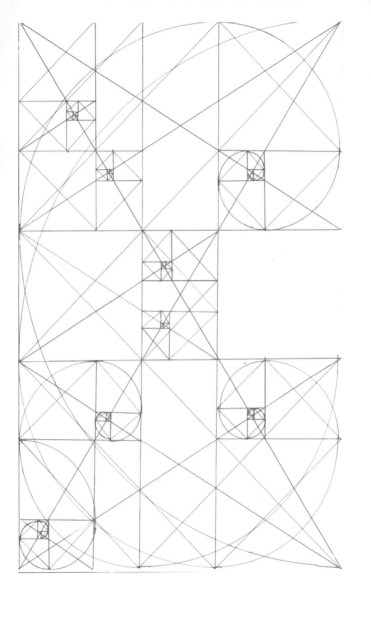

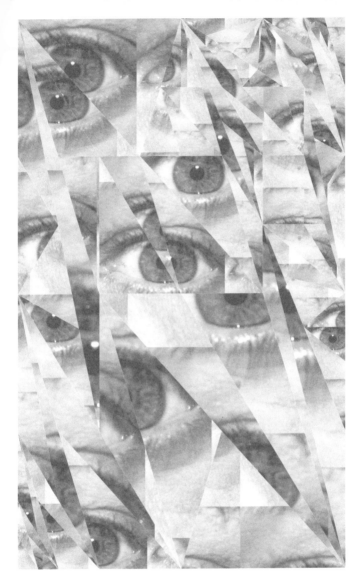

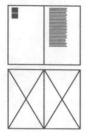

Angela Moore
UK

www.angela-moore.co.uk

I chose to communicate the golden ratio by illustrating how the Fibonacci numbers appear in nature.

I took a single leaf of clover and used mirrors to duplicate it and recreate its original form. The leaf is multiplied through reflection to produce the numbers in the Fibonacci sequence, (0, 1, 1, 2, 3, 5, 8...).

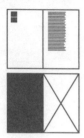

Hamish Muir
b1957/UK

www.hamishmuir.com

I'm interested in using numerical value
and simple rules to generate typographic
design: here the type size (height in mm)
and the interlinear spacing are based
on values from the Fibonacci sequence.

The type is aligned on a central axis
whose position was determined by dividing
the page width using the golden ratio.

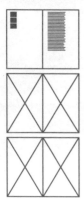

Jessica Nesbeth
b1990/UK

www.jessicanesbeth.co.uk

A series of hair arrangements illustrate
the unique proportions of the golden ratio.

short : long = long : (short + long)

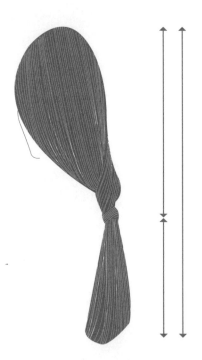

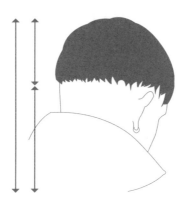

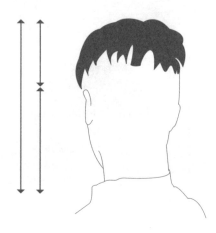

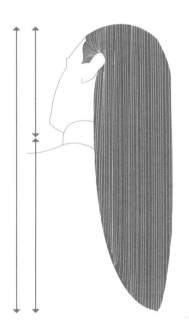

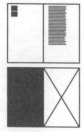

Nous Vous

Jay Cover
b1983/UK

www.nousvous.eu

───────

Having discovered a mind-boggling amount of visual material about the golden ratio, including what seemed like an infinite number of interpretations and explanations of it, we decided to follow our instincts and go for something simple.

We researched the work of some phi aficionados and enthusiasts and were left with the impression that the golden mean is deemed to have almost magical properties. We found it interesting how ubiquitous and pervasive phi is, as if it's a divine code for life, and considered how within the golden ratio people have found alternate methods of explaining existence – ones that are generally perceived to be at odds, such as spirituality and science, and mysticism and mathematics. The conflicts and contrasts between scientific and divine explanations struck us as a wonderful area to explore, a playground for thought and conversation on the subject.

Our box image not only shows a golden rectangle as a simple form, but also serves as a neat visual metaphor for packaging these opposing perspectives. Its form is domestic and human in scale. The 'math' box is in the process of being – or is already – unpacked, opened, explored, explained. The 'mystery' box sits underneath with its contents yet to be unpacked and revealed. We wanted to communicate that with every scientific discovery comes an abundance of new questions and that the world is a much richer, more wonderful place when it's filled with mystery.

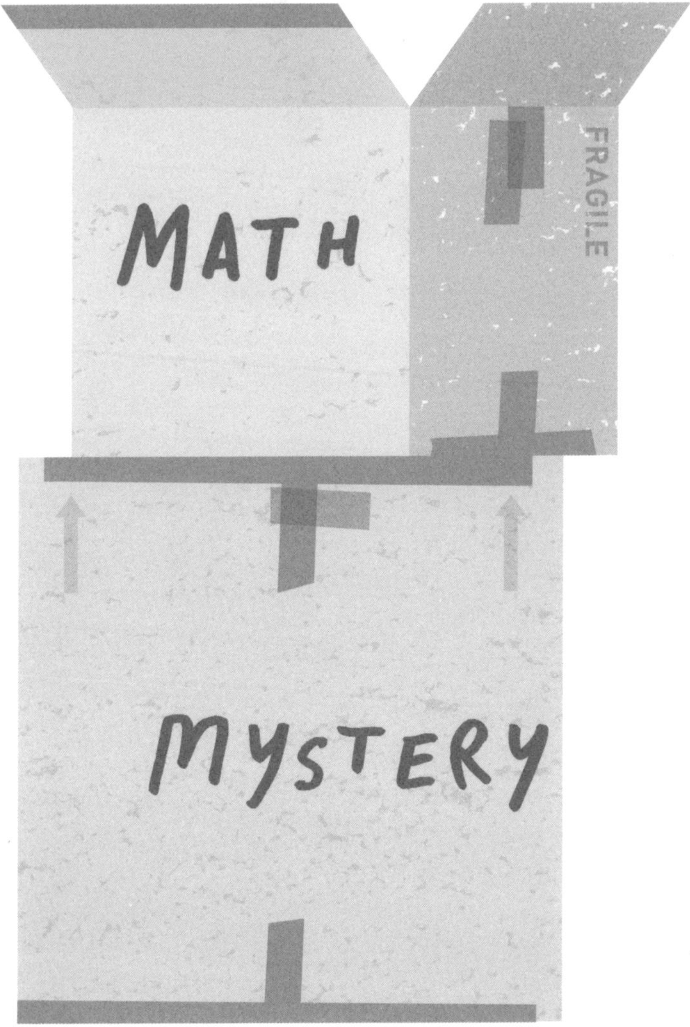
MATH
FRAGILE
MYSTERY

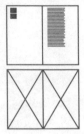

Eiko Ojala
b1982/Estonia

Lauri Tikerpe
b1975/Estonia

www.ploom.tv

What if the path to understanding the mean
is the mean itself?

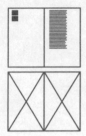

Vaughan Oliver
b1957/UK

Pixies: *Doolittle*
'5, 6, 7, Monkey's Gone to Heaven' was
the refrain on the supporting single.
Larbalestier shot the monkey. Who shot
the sheriff? I liked the challenge of using
exactly the same photo from that sleeve
and processing it to reflect the screenprint
medium. Meanwhile, Black Francis broke
my heart by telling me that successful
pop music was simply the intellectual
pursuit of good mathematics. Simple me
thought it all came from the heart. Then
I remembered that golden section theory
used in the composition of Renaissance
painting so I made my own grid to place
over the monkey.

Doolittle

PIXIES

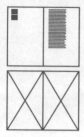

Peter Ørntoft
b1983/Denmark

www.peterorntoft.com

Why are humans so fascinated by the
Fibonacci sequence and the golden mean?
Various researchers in experimental
psychology have tested to see if we are
especially attracted by their aesthetic
properties. My project visualises a set
of research results from an investigation
carried out in 2009 by a group from
the University of Bamberg in Germany.
The research results are mapped on to
Vogel's model, a well-known visualisation
of the relationship between the pattern
of florets in sunflower heads and the
Fibonacci sequence.

All the dots in Vogel's model represent all the
test subjects in the sample. There are 358
dots and there were 267 subjects so this
is calculated by percentage: if 10% of the test
subjects liked the golden proportions then
10% of the dots reflect their response. The
different sized circles that surround each
dot in my diagram indicate how far the
test subjects were from preferring shapes
determined by the golden ratio. The smaller
the circle, the more the group favoured
these shapes. Had the entire group been
attracted to the shapes determined by
the golden ratio then my diagram would have
looked exactly the same as Vogel's model
but they didn't... Most subjects chose shapes
that had proportions that were close to, but
not the same as, those of the golden ratio,
so my diagram has morphed into a new
shape and in so doing visualises the subjects'
attraction to the aesthetic derived from
the golden ratio.

Vogel's Model (1979)

Golden section ⊙   *Golden section +/-1* ⊙

Großmann, Kärner, Maier, Räther, Reisinger, Sonnenberg,
Spindler, Witte, Yanenko, Stein & Schmid (2009)

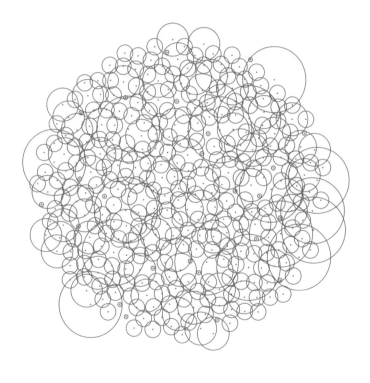

Golden section +/-2 *Golden section +/-3*

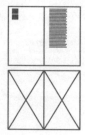

Present Perfect

Povilas Utovka
Ivan Markovic

www.presentperfect.co

We have built a grid using the Fibonacci
sequence, both horizontally and vertically.
We were interested to see if this would
create a harmonious sequence within the
golden rectangle that is the book's page.

We introduced gradients and converted
them to halftone bitmaps using a screen
angle of 137.5°, the golden angle, to add
depth and create a multi-dimensional effect.
This resulted in a series of optical illusions –
to the extent that the rectangles appear
to be curved.

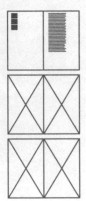

R2

Lizá Defossez Ramalho
b1971/France

Artur Rebelo
b1971/Portugal

www.r2design.pt

We decided to work with four digits in the Fibonacci sequence, liking the way that 1, 2, 3 appears to follow a logical pattern... but it is broken when 5 appears, instead of 4.

The numbers are created using golden rectangles that increase proportionally using the same sequence. The design of each number has been generated randomly using Processing.

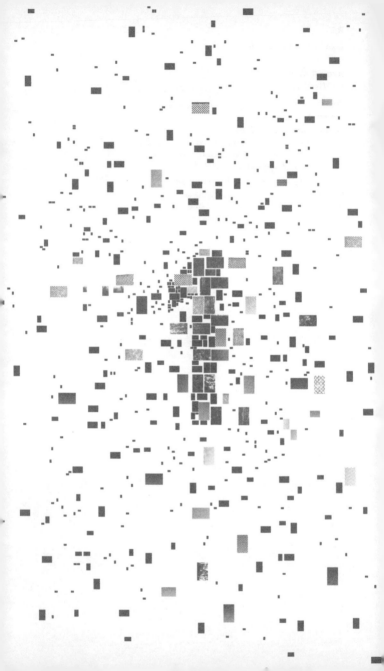

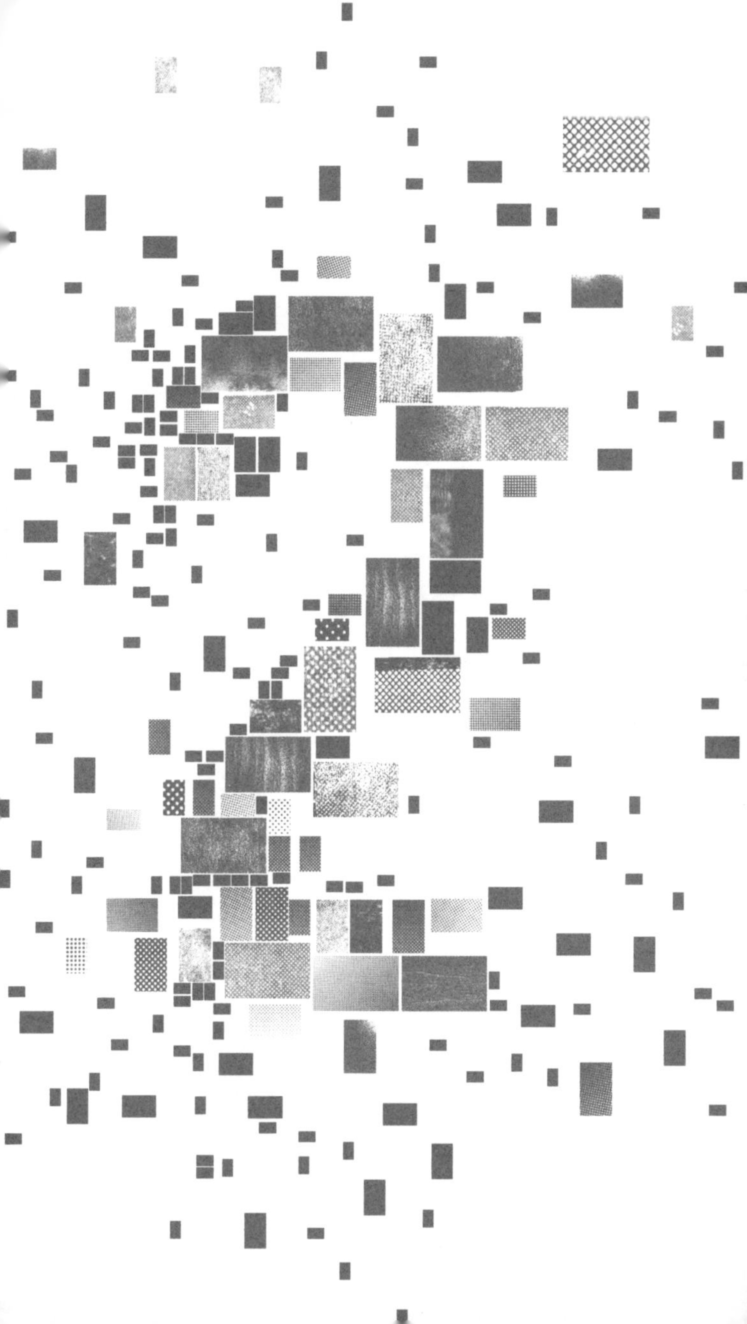

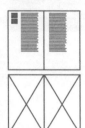

Sennep

Matt Rice
b1977/UK

Christoph Lorenzi
b1981/Germany

www.sennep.com

The connections between the golden ratio, Fibonacci numbers and the mesmerising patterns found in the head of the sunflower are fascinating. Our contribution pulls these elements together to highlight this magical sequence of numbers and their connection with growth, beauty and efficiency in nature. The golden angle (137.5°) is derived from the golden ratio and is responsible for the most compact arrangement of seeds in a sunflower head possible. The golden angle is calculated below:

$360° ÷ 1.618 = 222.5°$
$360° − 222.5° = 137.5°$

We found it intriguing that manipulating the golden angle by as little as 0.1° has a significant effect on both the aesthetics and efficiency of the seed layout. Our visualisation explores the impact of changing this angle. The 13 different angles we chose to create the different seed layouts were derived from the Fibonacci numbers, the most famous sequence in maths (0, 1, 1, 2, 3, 5, 8...). We were struck by the connection between the golden ratio and this sequence: when the ratios of consecutive Fibonacci numbers are arranged in a sequence their values increasingly approach the golden mean.

$\frac{1}{1}$	$\frac{2}{1}$	$\frac{3}{2}$	$\frac{5}{3}$	$\frac{8}{5}$	$\frac{13}{8}$	$\frac{21}{13}$	$\frac{34}{21}$	$\frac{55}{34}$
1	2	1.5	1.667	1.6	1.625	1.615	1.619	1.618

In the same way that the golden angle
is calculated using the golden ratio
(as demonstrated opposite) we derived
a progressive set of angles using these
Fibonacci ratios. To the nearest decimal
place, these were 0°, 180°, 120°, 144°, 135°,
138.5°, 137.1°, 137.6°, 137.5°. So for instance:

$$\frac{3}{2} = 1.5$$

360° ÷ 1.5 = 240°
360° − 240° = 120°

We put these angles into a mathematical
formula to generate the seed dispersal
within a fixed radius, with each composition
made up of 400 dots. The final formation
is made up of more than 6,000 dots,
which demonstrates how beautifully dense
the arrangement is when the golden angle
is used.

Our layout illustrates the distribution
of seeds inside a sunflower head moving
from rigid and inefficient formations to
a beautifully elegant arrangement. We
find it incredible that nature has evolved to
find this perfect arrangement. We hope our
contribution highlights how finely balanced
the mathematics behind it are, and how
closely the Fibonacci sequence is tied to
the golden ratio.

———————

To create the artwork, we coded a prototype:
goldenspiral.sennep.com

The Golden Ratio

$$\frac{1.618}{1}$$

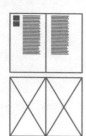

Natalie Sims
b1986/USA

www.nataliesims.com

The world is wide and yet it is like a home,
for the fire that burns in the soul is of
the same essential nature as the stars.

Georg Lukács
The Theory of the Novel
1914

A golden triangle has two long and one short side (its base), where the relationship between the shorter and longer side is equivalent to the golden ratio. This means that by bisecting one of the base angles, an identical smaller golden triangle is formed nestled inside, and that this process can be continued infinitely. Mapping the new vertices created by this process of bisecting will create a logarithmic spiral, a special kind of curve that also repeats in form, no matter how much you increase or decrease its scale. This golden spiral can be found in several natural phenomena that similarly vary in scale: from the chambers of a nautilus shell to the arms of the Milky Way.

I created a grid out of the form of the golden triangle. The grid lines multiply and fraction using the same elegant proportions as dictated by the golden spiral. This grid has no obvious beginning and could be repeated infinitely, were it not for the finitude of the pasteboard. The inherent limitation of my file created a bounded sample, offering a manageable chunk from which to enter into the scuffle.

The beauty of this pattern's potential for boundlessness is that even the most microscopic cove contains everything. And most thrilling of all: this is not a theory nor a model, but a cosmic code! A code that connects the very surface of our world with the most distant and unearthly galaxies. Inspired by this notion of cosmic symmetry, I created a series of dimensionless, multi-faceted shapes resembling both the familiarity of a mineral's crystal structure and the vagueness of an object, perhaps from outside our atmosphere.

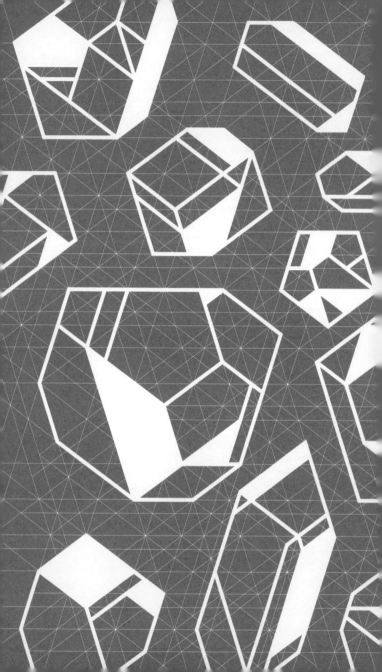

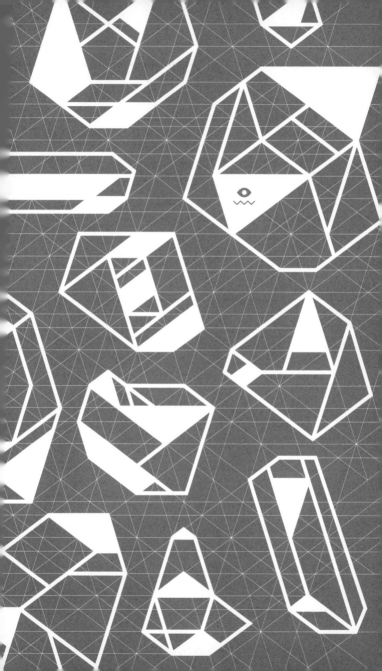

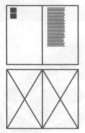

Talbot Type

Adrian Talbot
b1964/UK

www.talbottype.co.uk
www.intro-uk.com

As a type designer, the challenge of applying the golden mean to a typeface was one I felt I had to explore. What could be more effective for conveying the idea of the golden mean than a typeface designed according to its principles?

OK, the results are not that easy on the eye, but I wanted to use only a diagrammatic representation of the golden mean to make my point plainly.

Many typeface designs reference the golden mean for their proportions, particularly serif fonts. By way of a test, I compared the dimensions of several fonts to the dimensions defined by the golden mean, and found that the width, the x-height, the ascenders and descenders of many serif characters often match the golden mean.

However, none utilise the principles as precisely as this one; brutal it may be, but beautifully proportioned nonetheless.

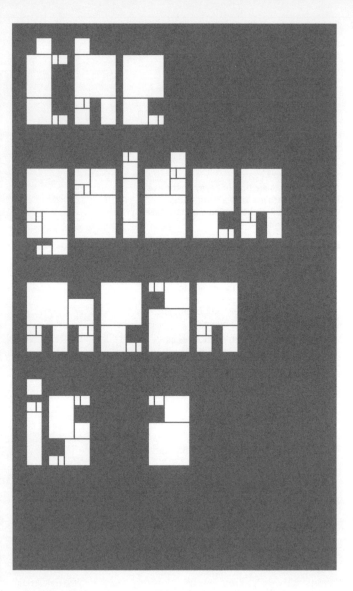

the golden mean is ?

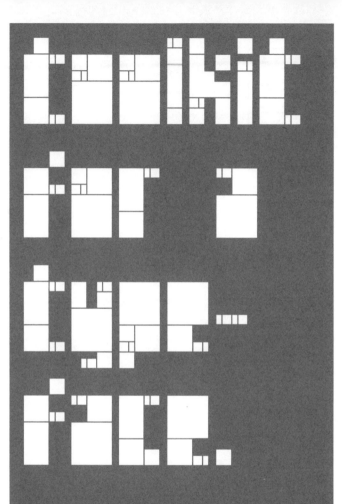

toolkit for a type-face.

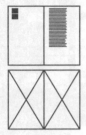

Clara Terne
b1983/Sweden

www.claraterne.com

———

I wanted to explore volume in my design
as most of the depictions that I found
during my research into the golden mean
represented it two-dimensionally only.
The golden ratio is commonly used in both
classical architecture and modern industrial
design so I was keen to represent it three-
dimensionally to reflect the importance
it plays in shaping products and buildings.
In my image all the shapes shown have
at least one side that uses the golden ratio
to determine its proportions.

My piece was constructed in a 3D program
environment where I gave the building
blocks varying material treatments. Gold
(golden ratio) made me think about applying
materials more generally, so my collection
of ratios appears to be made from rock, glass,
metal and graphite.

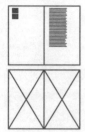

The Luxury of Protest

Peter Crnokrak
b1970/Croatia/Canada

www.theluxuryofprotest.com

———

Venus – the morning star – is the most visible celestial body in the sky after the Sun and the Moon and has played a key role in humankind's mythology and understanding of the cosmos. For centuries the study of celestial patterns has been considered dangerous, due largely to the view of the Catholic Church that the protosciences of astrology and alchemy were heresy and the work of the devil.

My Morning Star is a visual representation of the beauty of celestial geometry. The orbits of the Earth and Venus are in near-perfect 8:13 resonance – the Earth orbits the Sun eight times for every 13 orbits of Venus – creating a looping, pentagrammic pattern in space when viewed from the geocentric point of view of the Earth. The ratio 8:13 is a succession in the Fibonacci sequence and is closely approximated by the golden ratio. The resulting Earth/Venus orbital pentagrammic resonance pattern, when scaled at the golden ratio, perfectly subsumes within itself to form an infinitely scaled star fractal.

The intricate pattern seen here is entirely determined by the geometry of the golden ratio. The proportionate length of the arms of the stars, the internal angles of the lines and the relative scaling of star-to-star relationships and the resulting rosette-like clusters all conform to 1:1.61803… It's a testament to the stunning complexity that can arise from geometric simplicity.

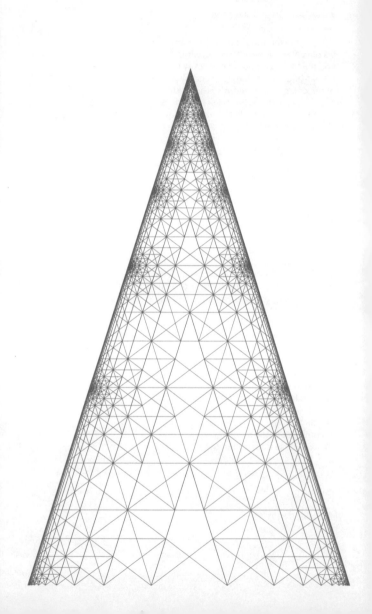

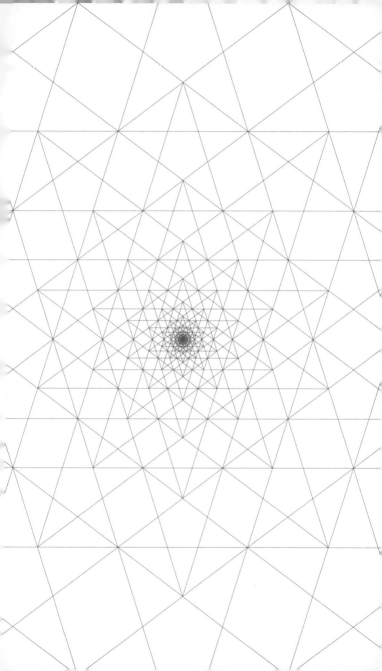

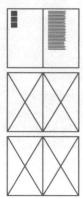

Ryan Todd
b1984/UK

www.ryantodd.com

———

When we recognise an object, the brain applies a detailed series of semantic attributes to it, including understanding its use, recalling previous experiences of it and remembering its relationship to other objects. I often subvert this process in my work. My images confound expectations to become memorable and illuminating.

For my response to the project, I've applied the golden mean to a series of common objects or symbols, modifying their appearance according to the golden ratio – and in so doing changing their meaning or sabotaging their ability to function. These humorous and playful alterations help the viewer not only to understand and remember the relative relationships of the ratio, but also to question its value and significance.

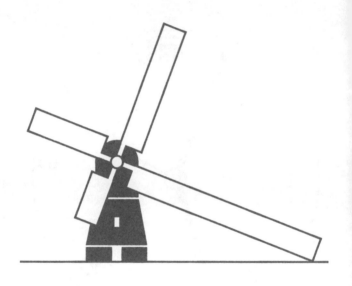

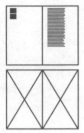

Geoff White
b1928/UK

I started this project by using diagrams
of the construction of the golden section
as the basis of my design. Some of the
images are shown on the right-hand page,
but I wasn't very happy with the results
so I decided to work in the way I usually do
and moved elements around until I arrived at
a satisfactory grouping. I started with some
rectangles, semicircles and lines and scaled
them according to the Fibonacci series
(shown in the key). In this way they were
related to one another, but I could position
them intuitively in my habitual manner.
The results are shown on the left-hand page.
Here, the curves of the semicircles echo
and oppose each other. The large dotted
semicircle represents the seeds on a
sunflower head, growing in two intersecting
spirals of 21 and 34, continuing the Fibonacci
theme. This also creates a contrasting texture
set against the adjoining flat tones. There
are three vertical bars and a set of diagonals
that contrast with the predominant
horizontals and verticals.

If you are interested in mathematical art, it
is worth looking at Swiss Concrete Art of the
1960s. This group of painter-designers aimed
to produce pictures where the size and
position of each shape was determined by
a system or programme. An important book
on this subject is *Designing Programmes*,
published in 1964 by Arthur Niggli.

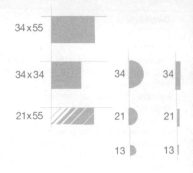

34 x 55

34 x 34   34   34

21 x 55   21   21

13   13

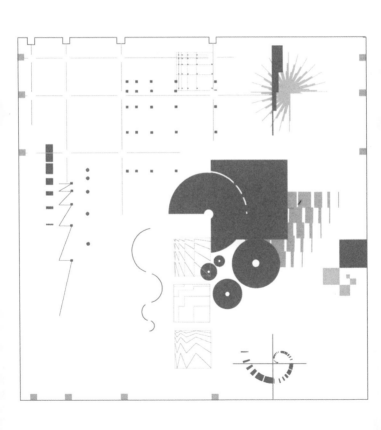

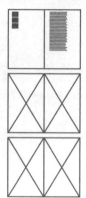

Ian Wright
b1953/UK

www.mrianwright.co.uk

———

Some close mates with deeper insight into song structure suggested a link explaining how the Fibonacci sequence relates to the structure of particular Beatles songs. Ready? 0, 1, 1, 2…

To me, even as a very young kid, The Beatles suggested a world of perfect harmony. I seemed to understand that they were much more than the sum of their individual parts – four independent musicians with very different personalities working together towards a common goal. I believed that they existed in a realm beyond the ordinary (the myth!), so much so that when I saw the film *Let It Be*, I felt totally disillusioned with them. They were so bitter with each other and not the happy family I had grown up with. I sold all my beloved Beatles LPs (except *Revolver*), only to buy them all back in desperation a couple of months later.

———

More on The Beatles and the golden mean:
http://goldensectionmusic.wordpress.com/the-big-list/

THE

BEATLES

INDEX

Brel   The Beatles   CS 148

Paul

BEATLES make a fuss of **RINGO**, whose birthday it was as he sits on **PAUL'S** shoulders to get level with **JOHN**, **GEORGE** supports his foot!

The Beatles

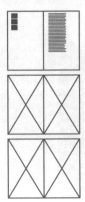

Yin Yao
b1989/China

www.yaoyindesign.com

The essential appeal of this project was that it gave me an opportunity not just to understand some aspects of the golden ratio, but also to represent or explore it visually from a new perspective. I wanted to avoid the usual visualisations of the golden ratio such as sunflower heads, the galaxy, seashells, *The Mona Lisa*, and so on.

The visualisation of the number itself (phi) is the main focus of my design. I wanted to express and display phi graphically using generative design. This method involves using a set of rules or an algorithm to generate the design. Phi is irrational, which means that its decimals keep going forever, never repeating the same pattern. I have used this idea to inform my design.

When we look at phi, it is comprised of two parts, the digit (1) and its decimals (.618...). Shown on the left-hand page of the second spread of my design is a small circle, which represents the digit, above a larger one, which represents the first 500 decimals of phi. Interestingly, despite the irrational nature of this number, it ultimately generates the harmonious form shown. The decimal system has 10 as its base so I divided the larger circle into 10 equal sections. I then connected each of the first 500 decimal numbers of phi in sequence. The opacity of each line is 10%, so the intensity of each line indicates the frequency of connections between any pair of numbers. The right-hand page shows this process.

1.618033988749894848204586834365638117720309179805762
8621354486227052604628189024497072072041893911374847 5
408807538689175212663386222353693179318006076672635 44
33389086595939582905638322661319928290267880675208766
892501711696207032221043216269548626296313614438149 75
87012203408058879544547492461856953648644492410443207
713449470495658467885098743394422125448770664780915 88
460749988712400765217057517978834166256249407589069 70
40002812104276217711117780531531714101170466659914669
7987317613560067087480710 1317952368942752194843530 56
78300228785699782977834784587822891109762500302696156
17002504643382437764861028383126833037249267526311 65
33924731671112115881863851331620384005222165791286675
29465490681131715993432359734949850904094762132229810
17261070596116456299098162905552085247903524060201727
99747117534277759277862561943208275051312181562855122 2
48093947123414517022373580577278616008688382952304592
64787801788992199027077690389532196819861514378031499
74110692608867429622675756052317277752035336139362107 6
738937645560606059216589466759551900400555908950229 53
09423124823552122124154440064703405657347976639723949
49946584578873039623090375033993856210242369025138680
41457799569812244574717803417312645322041639723213404
44494873023154176768937521030687378803441700939544096
27955898678723209512426893557309704509595684401755519
88192180206405290551893494759260073485228210108819464
454422231889131929468962200230144377026992300780308 52
61180754519288770502109684249362713592518760777884665
83615023891349333312231053392321362431926372891067050
33992822652635562090297986424727597725655086154875435
74826471814145127000602389016207773224499435308899909
50168032811219432048196438767586331479857191139781539
78074761507722117508269458639320456520989698555678141
06968372884058746103378105444390943683583581381131168
99385557697548414914453415091295407005019477548616307
54226417293946803673198058618339183285991303960720144
55950449779212076124785645916160837059498786006970189
40988640076443617093341727091914336501371576601148...

Visual representation
Golden ratio

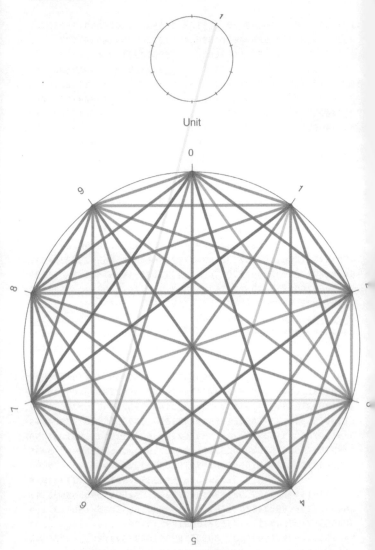

Unit

500 decimals of the golden ratio

Process of 500 decimals

1–50

51–100

101–150

151–200

201–250

251–300

301–350

351–400

401–450

451–500

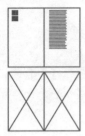

Catherine Zask

b1961/France

www.catherinezask.com

———

« Le grand sur le petit égale tout sur
le grand » énonce Mattias au milieu de
sa démonstration. Euh... répète ça ?
« Le grand sur le petit égale les deux sur
le grand » (- ::- ==;==) —Tu vois la scène ?
HAhahahhAAAh ! Allez je pars là-dessus,
c'est trop drôle, en anglais on dirait
comment ? "The big on the small equal
both on the big" _|_____> <>   ••[|-   ]
ça marche ! Perfect ! I'm on it, Sexy
Golden Number :)

$$\frac{\text{Le grand}}{\text{sur le petit}} = \frac{\text{les deux}}{\text{sur le grand}}$$

$$\frac{\text{The Big}}{\text{on the Small}} = \frac{\text{Both}}{\text{on the Big}}$$

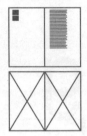

Lawrence Zeegen
b1964/UK

www.zeegen.com

A man nears the completion of creating
the perfect rectangular shape. The ratio
of the rectangle is 1:1.61803... He has created
a rectangle with proportions that relate
exactly to the golden mean. Is the man
a painter, art school-trained in the golden
section, or is the man simply a painter and
decorator with an innate sense of what
looks and feels right?

Biographies

Alex Bellos

Alex Bellos studied mathematics and philosophy at Corpus Christi College, Oxford University. From 1998 to 2003 he worked in Rio de Janeiro as *the Guardian*'s Brazil correspondent, and while there wrote *Futebol: The Brazilian Way of Life*. A regular contributor to Radio 4, Alex is also *the Guardian*'s maths blogger, and most recently the author of *Alex's Adventures in Numberland* [2010], shortlisted for the BBC Samuel Johnson Prize, a *New Scientist* book of the year and a *Sunday Times* bestseller. His book *Alex Through The Looking-Glass* is out in 2014.

Lucienne Roberts

Lucienne Roberts is a graphic designer and design writer. The work of her studio LucienneRoberts+ is defined by her intention to make accessible, engaging graphic design with a socially aware agenda. Lucienne's studio work spans exhibition design, books and corporate identity for the arts, cultural, publishing and public sectors. Her clients include London's Design Museum, Wellcome Collection and the British Council. Her books include *The Designer and the Grid* [2002, Rotovision] and *Good: An Introduction to Ethics in Graphic Design* [2006, AVA Academia]. She is a signatory of the *First Things First 2000* manifesto and a member of the Alliance Graphique Internationale.

Rebecca Wright

Rebecca Wright is Programme Director of Graphic Communication Design and Course Leader of MA Communication Design at Central Saint Martins, University of the Arts London. As a design educator and writer she has lectured, spoken at events and acted as consultant at academic institutions in the UK and abroad. She is currently writing a book on research methods in graphic design for Laurence King Publishing.

Lucienne and Rebecca co-wrote *Design Diaries: Creative Process in Graphic Design* [2010, Laurence King Publishing].

Thank you

to all our design contributors, who gave their time, ideas and expertise far more generously than we had any right to ask

and

Alex Bellos
Michael Czerwinski
Lorna Fray
James Grime
John McGill
Caroline Roberts
Caroline Walmsley
James Ward
Cerys Wilson

Rik van Leeuwen,
Paul van Mameren and
all the helpful team at
Lecturis BV

and

to our families who have continued to support us in what we hope will be a long and compelling endeavour:

Damian Wayling
Katy Roberts-Wayling
Ray Roberts

Lawrence Zeegen
Patrick Wright
Judy Wright